# The Money Magick Workbook

# Emme Rain

Lanico Media House
Celebrating literary lessons and legacies

Cover & Book design by Jesse Kimmel-Freeman

http://www.lanicomediahouse.com/

If you are unable to order this book from your local bookseller, you may order directly from the publisher.

ISBN: 978-0-9986520-7-8
10 9 8 7 6 5 4 3 2 1

Printed in the United States of America.

This journal is dedicated to my son, Montario Hampton, who first inspired me to get my financial shift together and change the direction of our bloodline. Because of him, I am wealthy. He was my first motivation, first supporter and the first to witness what has become our new family legacy, wealth and wisdom that shows up in business, investments and life in general.

# Acknowledgement

I'd like to first acknowledge Darlene Adams for gathering all the information for this money journal. She had to comb my classes, my posts, and prior programs. It was a lot of work, and we are grateful. I'd also like to acknowledge the Magickal Mystic staff who have played a major role in pushing me forward in every area, including the literary department. Nishisksi Chandler, thank you for pushing me to preserve my teachings in book and journal form. May the rise continue!

Thank you for choosing the Money Magick Workbook. If you apply the knowledge you learn within these pages, you will increase the flow of money into your life and keep it continuously flowing so that you reach your financial goals.

Money Magick is energy work specifically aimed at increasing abundance. Each week's assignment builds upon the previous week, allowing this journey to culminate with the mindset, vibration, tools, and plan to manifest the money and life you desire.

Money magick can and will change your life. All you need is commitment and consistency. Knowledge holds little value without application. Make the commitment that you will complete the weekly exercises. Some exercises you may need to adjust to ensure that what you are doing is in alignment with your personal energetic signature. Remember your journey will not be like anyone else's. Approach money magick as a fun journey that will become your lifestyle. Do this and money will always show up for you.

Let the journey begin!

# Week 1

## Mindset

The process of performing money magick can be correlated to farming. Farmers must prepare the soil before planting crops. They use nutrients and processes tailored specifically for the item that will be grown there. The process is the same with money magick. Your mind is the soil, the tools and techniques you learn during the following weeks are your nutrients and processes. The crop is money. Without the proper soil conditions your crop won't be bountiful, if it grows at all. The same with your mind. If your mind is filled with negative beliefs about money and you have a bad attitude towards wealth, then you won't be able to experience an abundant flow of money in your life. Most people don't truly know and understand their mindset concerning money. To understand and gauge where you're starting from on this journey, you need to know the answers to the following questions.

1. How do you feel about money?
2. What are your beliefs about money?
3. Do you understand the frequency of money?
4. How does it feel?
5. How does it smell?
6. What draws money in?
7. What repels it?
8. Does your current paradigm attract money to you?

A paradigm is all your beliefs about a topic. Your belief system surrounding money is usually formed in childhood. Do you believe that money is the root of all evil? Do you believe money is hard to come by, because you were told money doesn't grow on trees? You must dig into your past all the way back into your childhood and uncover all your beliefs around money.

Spend this week exploring your belief system. All the positive and negative. List them all below. Examine whether the belief is rooted in fear, love, lack/scarcity, or abundance. Anything that is not in alignment with abundance needs to be released and replaced in the coming weeks with a new paradigm that serves you. By performing these exercises, you will have an overall understanding of where you are beginning on your money magick journey. You will refer to this list in the coming weeks as you create a new paradigm and build a money magick lifestyle.

Do not feel disheartened or overwhelmed if you find you have a lengthy list of negative beliefs. In the coming weeks you will replace each one of these old negative beliefs with new beneficial ones by using the various techniques found in these pages. Pay attention to the negative beliefs that feel strongly rooted in your mind, you will create mantras and affirmations that address each one.

Positive beliefs about wealth and money.

_____

_____

_____

_____

_____

_____

_____

_____

_____

_____

_____

_____

_____

_____

_____

_____

Origins of your positive beliefs about wealth and money.

Negative beliefs about wealth and money.

_____

_____

_____

_____

_____

_____

_____

_____

_____

_____

_____

_____

_____

_____

_____

Origins of your negative beliefs about wealth and money.

_____

_____

_____

_____

_____

_____

_____

_____

_____

_____

_____

_____

_____

_____

_____

Now that you have a clearer understanding of your current money paradigm and its origins, we will begin the process of shifting it into alignment with what you desire. This is done by releasing any current beliefs you have that are working against you and replacing them with new beliefs that will attract a continuous flow of money into your life.

How do you think your current paradigm has affected the flow of money in your life? Are you ready to release it?

_____

_____

_____

_____

_____

_____

_____

_____

_____

_____

_____

_____

_____

# Week 2

## Setting Intentions and Gaining Clarity

Clarity is integral to the success of your money magick. Most people are too vague. They make abstract statements like I want to be rich. There is no clearly defined target within that statement. What does it mean to be rich? How much money does that require? Without creating a definitive goal, it is more difficult to achieve success and maintain it. Without clarity you are more susceptible to the two major barriers people have when doing money magick. Doubt and impatience. Many people have a difficult time believing in money magick and when they try to perform it, they are anxious and desperate. Desperation begets more desperation. They are unable to experience its effectiveness because they try to produce money immediately, through a method they are skeptical about. When you start your money magick journey, it is imperative that you set clear, attainable, yet challenging goals. The first goal is the most important. If it is too far out of alignment with your current beliefs and circumstances, then it will be much more difficult energetically to bring to fruition. If your goal is to be a multimillionaire but you're currently making $40,000 per year. The distance between where you are and where you want to be is so great that the likelihood of you becoming discouraged and giving up is increased. I recommend breaking down larger target amounts into monthly amounts. As you reach each checkpoint and have proof of power with your money magick, steadily increase your amounts until you achieve your original target. Then keep going!

Sometimes, you begin the journey and realize that you need more. That's fine. It's okay if right now you begin with $5,000 per month and start working toward it just to get there and discover you need more. The fact that you got there at all is powerful and it provides the fuel to get to the next place. On the other hand, sometimes you will begin and it will seem as though everything is telling you there is no way for you to do better than you are currently. When that kind of doubt rears its ugly head, coming back to your workbook can be very powerful. Incorporating money mantras and affirmations will also alleviate the agony of doubt. One of my favorite mantras for this week is: I am clear about and committed to living in abundance.

To manifest using money magick you need to set your intention and commit to doing whatever it takes mentally, energetically, and physically to reach your goals.

This week sit with yourself and clarify what your money objectives are.

How much do you want to bring in monthly?

_____

_____

_____

_____

_____

How much money do you want to bring in next year?

_____

_____

_____

_____

_____

Do you want a new car? Describe the car you want in detail.

Do you want a new home? Describe the home you want in great detail.

_____

_____

_____

_____

_____

_____

_____

_____

_____

Do you want to have your own business? Describe the business you want to own in detail.

_____

_____

_____

_____

_____

_____

_____

_____

_____

_____

_____

_____

_____

_____

_____

_____

_____

What kind of lifestyle do you want to live? Describe it in detail.

_____

_____

_____

_____

_____

_____

# Week 3

## Getting into the Vibration

You spent the previous weeks identifying where you are and where you want to be. Now it's time to begin the process of shifting your vibration to align with your desires. In week one, you identified all the positive and negative beliefs that create your paradigm around money. All your negative beliefs must be released and replaced with new beliefs that are in direct alignment with your monetary goals. Presently, all your negative beliefs are causing resistance and prohibiting you from amassing wealth. You will spend the next few weeks familiarizing yourself with the vibration of abundance. You will create new beliefs based on the knowledge you gain from being in environments where you learn how abundance smells, tastes, sounds, looks, and feels.

The best way to get into the vibration of money is to intentionally put yourself in environments that are monetarily abundant or have elements of abundance that match your desires. Surround yourself with people that are abundant and opulent. Drive around a wealthy neighborhood. Park in front of houses that are for sale and walk up to the door as if you are going home. Browse the most expensive stores as if you belong there. Touch the items. Try things on. Visualize yourself owning them. Join groups whose members are living the lifestyle you want to live. It's all right if it starts virtually, as your magick grows so will your relationships and social circles. Go to country clubs, political rallies, and the Chamber of Commerce. Shake hands with business owners and other people of influence. Go to expensive restaurants, even if you only order a salad and water. Everywhere you go, you want to absorb the energy of abundance from your environment.

This week spend at least 30 minutes each day in an abundant environment. Enjoy it and absorb it. Each day write down your impressions. Engage all five of your senses. Really focus on how it felt. Did you experience any emotional reactions? You want to be as detailed as possible, you are writing how you experience the vibration and frequency of money.

# Day One

List the environment you were in and your impressions. Be sure to write about all your sensory and emotional responses.

_____

_____

_____

_____

_____

_____

_____

_____

_____

_____

_____

_____

# Day Two

List the environment you were in and your impressions. Be sure to write about all your sensory and emotional responses.

_____

_____

_____

_____

_____

_____

_____

_____

_____

_____

_____

_____

_____

_____

_____

# Day Three

List the environment you were in and your impressions. Be sure to write about all your sensory and emotional responses.

_____

_____

_____

_____

_____

_____

_____

_____

_____

_____

_____

_____

_____

_____

# Day Four

List the environment you were in and your impressions. Be sure to write about all your sensory and emotional responses.

_____

_____

_____

_____

_____

_____

_____

_____

_____

_____

_____

_____

_____

_____

_____

_____

_____

_____

_____

_____

_____

_____

# Day Five

List the environment you were in and your impressions. Be sure to write about all your sensory and emotional responses.

_____

_____

_____

_____

_____

_____

_____

_____

_____

_____

_____

_____

_____

_____

# Day Six

List the environment you were in and your impressions. Be sure to write about all your sensory and emotional responses.

_____

_____

_____

_____

_____

_____

_____

_____

_____

_____

_____

_____

_____

_____

_____

_____

# Day Seven

List the environment you were in and your impressions. Be sure to write about all your sensory and emotional responses.

# Week 4

## Using the Elements to Shift Your Vibration & Mindset

In week one you created a list of beliefs and identified which ones will not serve your future self. Last week you spent time familiarizing yourself with the vibration of money. You are now ready to release those negative beliefs and replace them with new beliefs that match the vibration of your money magick goals.

In the coming weeks you will learn to use the elements as tools to release and then replace any non-beneficial parts of your money paradigm.

We will focus on the four elements of earth, air, fire, and water. Each week you will be working with an element to learn techniques to release negative beliefs and replace them with beneficial ones. Remember you are the magick and the ways that you use the elements are limited only by your intention and imagination. As you become more aligned with wealth and more confident with your money magick, the ways you use the elements will expand. You will naturally become familiar with more tools and resources, such as how to use the energy of the days of the week, the planets, deities, and other energies. The four basic elements are just a starting point. Everyone has access to at least one representation of each element.

As you study and get to know each element and how it relates to money, allow your mind to expand beyond the obvious uses for the elements. Examine how the elements like to show up in the world and build upon that.

You may feel at this point that you aren't practicing magick. I assure you every step you've taken this far has been pure magick because you are the magick. Each step you take to elevate yourself is magick. The work you've done in the previous weeks enables the magick you do from now on, to be more powerful and effective. Before we get into working with the elements take some time this week to reflect on your journey so far.

Have you felt a shift in your relationship with money? If so, in what way?

_____

_____

_____

_____

_____

_____

_____

_____

_____

_____

_____

_____

_____

_____

Are you thinking of new ways to create streams of income? If so, write them here.

As you've been doing the work each week you may have noticed unexpected opportunities and money are beginning to flow into your life. This is your proof of power. List them here. If there are opportunities of increase that are in alignment with your desires, take advantage of them. I recommend do this as soon as possible. Inspired action is one of the greatest drivers of success.

Unexpected opportunities and money you've received.

_____

_____

_____

_____

_____

_____

_____

_____

_____

_____

_____

_____

# Week 5

## Water

Water is the element of nourishment. It is a cleanser and conductor. Incorporating water into your money magick is simple. It is a matter of performing your daily activities with intention. As a tool to release, before your shower or bath you will set the intention that you will be cleansed and renewed by the time you step out. While you are washing your body, you will envision the water purifying you of past mistakes with money. See it washing away the poverty mentality, overspending, and all the other things you need to release. See it all go down the drain.

Next, allow the water to replenish and nourish you. Feel the seeds of prosperity and abundance being watered. Nourish the parts of you that believe you are worth abundance and the life you desire to live.

You can also program your water. Any negativity you have towards money speak it into a glass of water. You can say things like, *I never have enough money. As soon as I get money something happens, and I have to spend it.* After speaking every thought, action, and belief you want to release into the water pour the glass of water into the earth. Releasing it to never be a part of you again.

Before drinking water, speak your positive intentions into it. Hold it as you envision those intentions becoming reality. You can write it down and tape it to your bottle before putting it in the refrigerator. Once you drink it, your body will be infused with all the energy of your intentions.

These are just a few examples of how to use water. Spend this week exploring all the ways you can incorporate water into your money magick. Once you have completed your list, commit to doing at least one thing each day.

_____

_____

What was your experience working with the element of water? Do you feel a strong connection to the element?

_____

_____

_____

_____

_____

_____

_____

_____

_____

_____

_____

_____

_____

_____

_____

_____

What expected and unexpected money and opportunities have you received this week?

_____

_____

_____

_____

_____

_____

_____

_____

_____

_____

_____

_____

_____

# Week 6

## Air

Air is the element of intelligence. It is communication and it is the breath. When performing money magick, using the element of air may be your most powerful tool in changing your mindset. The normal act of breathing is an act of releasing and replacing. Every inhale you are absorbing something and with every exhale you are releasing something. If you begin to breathe with magickal intention you can exhale and release what no longer serves you and inhale beneficial energy to assist you with your goals in its place.

Incense, mantras, and affirmations are all forms of air magick. Mantras are sounds or phrases that carry a vibration to get you in agreement with what you desire. Mantras are created in the present tense. It helps to reprogram the subconscious and to align the conscious and subconscious mind. They are the most effective when done daily as a practice for 108 or more repetitions. You can whisper them, sing them, or simply speak them.

Affirmations are powerful positive statements that are declared with authority. They are a proclamation. Think of them like a divine directive, a projection of power to establish fact. Both mantras and affirmations are tools to assist you in reprogramming your mind to improve and accept yourself, as well as achieve your goals. However, while mantras are directed within, affirmations are powerful because they shift the aura and flow of your energy and call forth external agreement due to that shift. Together, they represent "As above, so below" as they shift your internal and external reality.

This week you are creating mantras for your money magick journey. As you create your mantras use your list from week one to create mantras that address your mindset issues, especially around fear and lack. Your mantras should use words or phrases that are a normal part of your vocabulary and resonate with you. Here are some examples of money mantras.

*I am in agreement with abundance.*
*Money flows easily to me.*
*I am financially free.*

Mantras are most effective when repeated 108 times and as each mantra becomes a part of your subconscious mind you want to continue to build on them. Create a new story for your life, one that is filled with wealth and all that you desire.

Create mantras to work with for the next 7 days. You may use the examples in the book or create your own. Make sure they reflect your future self.

What was your experience working with your mantras? Do you feel a shift in your vibration? How so?

_____

_____

_____

_____

_____

_____

_____

_____

_____

What expected and unexpected money and opportunities have you received this week?

_____

_____

_____

_____

_____

_____

_____

# Week 7

## Affirmations

Last week you worked with mantras which are focused on repetition. This week you will be working with affirmations which focus on putting power and authority into your voice as you say them frequently throughout your day.

You are declaring to yourself and the Universe that what you say is true. Affirmations are also written in the present tense. The key when saying your affirmations is believing it is already done. Here are some examples of money affirmations.

*I affirm I allow money to flow into my life.*
*I affirm my life is full of opportunities for abundance.*
*I affirm I choose money, and money also chooses me.*

Your assignment this week is to create an affirmation for each day of the week that corresponds to the mantras you are saying. Focus on infusing power into your voice. Say them often throughout your day.

_____

_____

_____

_____

_____

What was your experience working with your affirmations? Do you feel a shift in your vibration? How so?

_____

_____

_____

_____

_____

_____

What expected and unexpected money and opportunities have you received this week?

_____

_____

_____

_____

_____

_____

_____

_____

_____

_____

_____

_____

# Week 8

## Earth

Earth is the energy of grounding, support, and growth. Earth is the element of foundation. Earth magick uses tools like crystals, herbs, roots, stones, metals, and dirt.

One way to use earth to release what no longer serves you is to stand in your yard and visualize all negative thoughts and beliefs being funneled into the ground. Or you can take a more elaborate route and have a funeral service for your old self and burying all the old beliefs and habits that stood between you and the life you desire.

Earth has the benefit of being a highly tangible element with each representation having its own inherent energy signature. Some crystals, herbs, and metals have an affinity for money and wealth work. Gold, silver, citrine, basil, mint, and cinnamon are all examples of powerful earth elements related to money. This is your money magick journey, so whatever represents money and wealth to you are all good items to use. If it makes you feel abundant then use it. Dirt from a bank, jewelry, precious stones are all great tools. You can dress a candle with herbs and oils that represent money, or carry stones like citrine with you. It is all about your intentions.

Create a list of all the ways you can use earth on your money magick journey. Commit to doing at least one thing every day for the next 7 days.

What was your experience working with the element of earth? Do you feel a strong connection to the element?

_____

_____

What expected and unexpected money and opportunities have you received this week?

_____

_____

_____

_____

_____

_____

_____

_____

_____

_____

_____

_____

_____

_____

# Week 9

## Fire

Fire is the spark of life. It is passion, and movement. It is the element of initiation. Also, it is an element of purification. Fire magick is the most popular and well-known form of magick. Everyone is familiar with burning a candle for spell or ritual work.

When using the element of fire to release, you will focus on the purification aspect of fire. Writing out your old paradigms and habits that you want to release and then burning them is a fantastic way of releasing. A fire ritual of release can be simple or elaborate, but it carries a finality that few other things do when it comes to transmutation of what you were and what you hope to be.

Once you burn what no longer serves you, write out your new paradigm and place a candle on top of it, setting your intention that as the candle burns, you are embodying everything you wrote. Other great ways to work with the fire element besides candles, are fireplaces, fire pits, volcano ash for a blended earth/fire combo, and the sun. You can release with the sunset and replace with the sunrise. You also can sit and absorb the energy.

This week, list all the ways you can think of to include fire in your money magick journey and commit to doing at least one thing on your list each day this week. Please always practice fire safety.

What was your experience working with the element of fire? Do you feel a strong connection to the element?

_____

_____

What expected and unexpected money and opportunities have you received this week?

_____

_____

_____

_____

_____

_____

_____

_____

_____

_____

_____

_____

# Week 10

## Visualization

Visualization is a powerful manifestation tool. It is the act of creating vivid and captivating images in your mind that invoke an emotional response from you. Visualization should be used in combination with all other techniques. Every time you wash your body, eat, drink, light a candle, say a mantra or affirmation you should be visualizing your intention.

If you are working towards a new car, you should not only be envisioning the make, model, year, and color but you should employ all your senses and create entire scenarios. How do the seats feel when you sit in it? What does your car smell like? How do your hands feel on the steering wheel? What does it sound like? Do you have a quiet and smooth ride? Or a loud powerful one. See yourself washing it. When visualizing you want to be so detailed that your emotions can't help but respond to what you are creating in your mind's eye. You want to feel the joy, excitement, peace, and freedom. When you are manifesting a certain dollar amount focus on the activities it will allow you to do. Money likes to flow. Envision how you will move it in your life. Traveling, your dream home, a new business, a new car, paying off debt? If you are emotionally responding, then your manifestation and you are in agreement and aligned.

Focusing on visualization is easier if you write it out. You can write out in great detail what you want, what you will do when you manifest your desire, and how you feel about having it. Read it every day, multiple times of day. Great times to practice visualization as a manifestation tool by itself, are first thing in the morning and right before you fall asleep at night.

This week intentionally include visualization while performing your other money magick activities. Visualize while you are eating, drinking, bathing, and doing your mantras and affirmations.

Write out a detailed scenario about how you will interact with your manifestation. If it's a new home, it can be cooking in your kitchen. If it's a new car it could be driving it through your favorite neighborhood. If it's a sum of money for a trip see yourself at the location and enjoying an activity. Or you can see yourself writing checks to clear your debt. Whatever you choose, read over it, at least one time a day either right after waking or right before going to sleep and spend 15 minutes focused solely on visualizing your target. Be sure you are incorporating all 5 senses and feel emotionally engaged with your visualization.

_____

_____

_____

_____

_____

_____

_____

_____

_____

_____

# Week 11

## A Word About Ritual

Ritual can be defined as a series of actions or type of behavior regularly and invariably followed by someone. We all have rituals, and the purpose of this 12-week journey is to make money magick a lifestyle filled with daily rituals dedicated to attracting money into your life. Consistency and mindfulness are what powers your magick, but that doesn't mean you shouldn't perform more elaborate ceremonial actions. It just means it's not necessary to be successful.

As you become more open and aware of magick and its plethora of tools, you may come to learn about energies related to the days of the week, planets, and seasons. You may come to learn about moon and solar cycles, retrogrades, and personal life cycles. You may explore working with deities, angels and other energies associated with wealth. All these are valid and powerful aids on your money magick journey. Feel free to incorporate them into your practice as often and as grand as you like. If you feel inspired to create a multi-candle ritual invoking various energies, then do so. I recommend you devote at least one day a week to perform a candle ritual and charge all your herbs, crystals, water, and other consumables you use in your money magick work. In this case more is more if you are consistent.

Your assignment this week is to create a money magick ritual. Incorporate as many elements as you like. There are rituals on the Magickal Mystic Facebook business page, @themagickalmystic, that you can use for inspiration. Be free with your ritual. Be imaginative. Trust your intuition and have fun. If you are using candles remember to always practice fire safety. You may also want to get the SpiRitual Gangsta book to learn more about ritual and incorporate a lot of the amazing information in it.

What did you petition for during your ritual?

_____

_____

_____

_____

_____

_____

_____

_____

_____

_____

_____

_____

_____

_____

What feelings and thoughts came to you as you sat with your ritual?

_____

_____

_____

Write down any messages, dreams, and inspirations that you experienced during and after your ritual was complete.

_____

_____

_____

_____

_____

_____

_____

_____

_____

_____

_____

_____

# Week 12

## The Plan

You've begun experiencing the vibration and frequency of money. You've learned about yourself and what causes resistance to money flowing into your life. You've experimented and worked with the elements. You should have a list of mantras and affirmations that you've customized for what you want to manifest. This week you are going to take what you've learned and create a plan. Remember your objective is for money magick to become a lifestyle.

If you've been consistent with your exercises, then you should already be experiencing an increase in money flowing into your life. You should also have more opportunities for increase being presented to you as well. Opportunities for investments, higher paying positions, and business partnerships.

To understand what works for you look back over the previous sections. Make note of what weeks you experienced the most increase. What activities felt most aligned with your target goal? What days of the week felt most powerful to you? Why do you think that is? What environments made you feel the most connected to the frequency of money? In other words, what environments did you feel wealthy in? What environments did you feel most comfortable networking in? What elemental activities did you feel were most effective in helping you release your negative beliefs and habits? What elemental activities do you feel were most effective in helping you create new beneficial beliefs to replace your negative ones? Were there certain days of the week that you felt more aligned with your money magick?

Answering these questions will give you the insight and tools you need to create a 30-day plan for your money magick. You don't need to do something different every day. You want to do what works every day.

Having a plan already mapped out allows you to put energy into the activity versus wasting energy everyday trying to figure out what you're going to do.

Create your money magick plan of action for the next 30 days.

## Day One

What abundant environment will you visit?

_____

_____

_____

_____

_____

_____

_____

_____

_____

_____

What is your daily mantra?

_____

_____

_____

_____

What is your daily affirmation?

_____

_____

_____

_____

How will you use water to release what doesn't serve you?

_____

_____

_____

_____

_____

_____

_____

_____

How will you use water to replace the negative with something beneficial?

_____

_____

_____

_____

_____

_____

_____

How will you use air to release what doesn't serve you?

_____

_____

_____

_____

_____

_____

_____

_____

_____

How will you use air to replace the negative with something beneficial?

_____

_____

_____

_____

_____

_____

_____

How will you use earth to release what doesn't serve you?

_____

_____

_____

_____

_____

_____

_____

How will you use earth to replace the negative with something beneficial?

_____

_____

_____

_____

_____

_____

_____

_____

How will you use fire to release what doesn't serve you?

_____

_____

_____

_____

_____

_____

_____

_____

How will you use fire to replace the negative with something beneficial?

_____

_____

_____

_____

_____

_____

_____

_____

Write your visualization that you are using to help manifest your goal.

_____

_____

_____

_____

_____

_____

_____

# Day Two

What abundant environment will you visit?

_____

_____

_____

_____

_____

_____

_____

_____

_____

_____

What is your daily mantra?

_____

_____

_____

What is your daily affirmation?

_____

_____

_____

_____

How will you use water to release what doesn't serve you?

_____

_____

_____

_____

_____

_____

_____

_____

How will you use water to replace the negative with something beneficial?

_____

_____

_____

_____

_____

How will you use air to release what doesn't serve you?

How will you use air to replace the negative with something beneficial?

_____

_____

_____

_____

_____

How will you use earth to release what doesn't serve you?

_____

_____

_____

_____

_____

_____

_____

_____

How will you use earth to replace the negative with something beneficial?

_____

_____

_____

_____

_____

How will you use fire to release what doesn't serve you?

How will you use fire to replace the negative with something beneficial?

_____

_____

_____

_____

_____

_____

_____

Write your visualization that you are using to help manifest your goal.

_____

_____

_____

_____

_____

_____

_____

_____

## Day Three

What abundant environment will you visit?

_____

_____

_____

_____

_____

_____

_____

_____

_____

_____

_____

_____

What is your daily mantra?

_____

_____

_____

What is your daily affirmation?

_____

_____

_____

How will you use water to release what doesn't serve you?

_____

_____

_____

_____

_____

_____

_____

_____

How will you use water to replace the negative with something beneficial?

_____

_____

_____

_____

_____

_____

_____

How will you use air to release what doesn't serve you?

_____

_____

_____

_____

_____

_____

_____

_____

How will you use air to replace the negative with something beneficial?

_____

_____

_____

_____

_____

_____

_____

How will you use earth to release what doesn't serve you?

How will you use earth to replace the negative with something beneficial?

_____

_____

_____

How will you use fire to release what doesn't serve you?

_____

_____

_____

_____

_____

_____

_____

How will you use fire to replace the negative with something beneficial?

_____

_____

_____

_____

_____

_____

_____

_____

_____

_____

Write your visualization that you are using to help manifest your goal.

_____

_____

_____

_____

_____

_____

## Day Four

What abundant environment will you visit?

_____

_____

_____

_____

_____

_____

_____

_____

_____

_____

_____

_____

What is your daily mantra?

_____

_____

_____

What is your daily affirmation?

_____

_____

_____

How will you use water to release what doesn't serve you?

_____

_____

_____

_____

_____

_____

_____

_____

How will you use water to replace the negative with something beneficial?

_____

_____

_____

_____

_____

_____

How will you use air to release what doesn't serve you?

_____

_____

_____

How will you use air to replace the negative with something beneficial?

How will you use earth to release what doesn't serve you?

How will you use earth to replace the negative with something beneficial?

How will you use fire to release what doesn't serve you?

_____

_____

_____

_____

_____

_____

_____

How will you use fire to replace the negative with something beneficial?

_____

_____

_____

_____

_____

_____

_____

_____

_____

Write your visualization that you are using to help manifest your goal.

_____

_____

_____

_____

_____

_____

_____

## Day Five

What abundant environment will you visit?

_____

_____

_____

_____

_____

_____

_____

_____

_____

_____

_____

_____

What is your daily mantra?

_____

_____

_____

What is your daily affirmation?

_____

_____

_____

How will you use water to release what doesn't serve you?

_____

_____

_____

_____

_____

_____

_____

_____

_____

How will you use water to replace the negative with something beneficial?

_____

_____

_____

_____

_____

_____

How will you use air to release what doesn't serve you?

_____

_____

_____

_____

_____

_____

_____

_____

_____

_____

How will you use air to replace the negative with something beneficial?

_____

_____

_____

_____

_____

_____

_____

How will you use earth to release what doesn't serve you?

_____

_____

_____

_____

_____

_____

_____

_____

_____

_____

_____

How will you use earth to replace the negative with something beneficial?

_____

_____

_____

_____

_____

_____

_____

_____

How will you use fire to release what doesn't serve you?

_____

_____

_____

_____

_____

_____

_____

_____

_____

How will you use fire to replace the negative with something beneficial?

_____

_____

_____

_____

_____

_____

_____

Write your visualization that you are using to help manifest your goal.

_____

_____

_____

_____

_____

_____

_____

_____

_____

# Day Six

What abundant environment will you visit?

_____

_____

_____

_____

_____

_____

_____

_____

What is your daily mantra?

What is your daily affirmation?

How will you use water to release what doesn't serve you?

How will you use water to replace the negative with something beneficial?

_____

_____

_____

_____

_____

_____

_____

How will you use air to release what doesn't serve you?

_____

_____

_____

_____

_____

_____

_____

_____

How will you use air to replace the negative with something beneficial?

How will you use earth to release what doesn't serve you?

How will you use earth to replace the negative with something beneficial?

_____

_____

_____

_____

_____

_____

_____

_____

How will you use fire to release what doesn't serve you?

_____

_____

_____

_____

_____

_____

_____

_____

_____

How will you use fire to replace the negative with something beneficial?

_____

_____

_____

_____

_____

_____

_____

Write your visualization that you are using to help manifest your goal.

_____

_____

_____

_____

_____

_____

_____

_____

_____

## Day Seven

What abundant environment will you visit?

_____

_____

_____

_____

_____

_____

_____

_____

_____

_____

_____

What is your daily mantra?

_____

_____

_____

_____

What is your daily affirmation?

_____

_____

_____

_____

How will you use water to release what doesn't serve you?

_____

_____

_____

_____

_____

_____

_____

_____

How will you use water to replace the negative with something beneficial?

_____

_____

_____

_____

_____

_____

_____

How will you use air to release what doesn't serve you?

_____

_____

_____

_____

_____

_____

_____

_____

_____

How will you use air to replace the negative with something beneficial?

_____

_____

_____

_____

_____

_____

_____

_____

How will you use earth to release what doesn't serve you?

_____

_____

_____

_____

_____

_____

_____

_____

How will you use earth to replace the negative with something beneficial?

_____

_____

_____

_____

_____

_____

_____

_____

How will you use fire to release what doesn't serve you?

_____

_____

_____

_____

_____

_____

_____

_____

How will you use fire to replace the negative with something beneficial?

_____

_____

_____

_____

_____

_____

_____

_____

Write your visualization that you are using to help manifest your goal.

_____

_____

_____

_____

_____

_____

_____

# Day Eight

What abundant environment will you visit?

_____

_____

_____

_____

_____

_____

_____

_____

_____

What is your daily mantra?

_____

_____

_____

_____

What is your daily affirmation?

_____

_____

_____

_____

How will you use water to release what doesn't serve you?

_____

_____

_____

_____

_____

_____

_____

How will you use water to replace the negative with something beneficial?

_____

_____

_____

_____

_____

_____

_____

_____

_____

How will you use air to release what doesn't serve you?

_____

_____

_____

_____

_____

_____

_____

_____

How will you use air to replace the negative with something beneficial?

_____

_____

_____

_____

_____

_____

_____

_____

_____

How will you use earth to release what doesn't serve you?

_____

_____

_____

_____

_____

_____

_____

_____

How will you use earth to replace the negative with something beneficial?

_____

_____

_____

_____

_____

_____

_____

_____

_____

_____

How will you use fire to release what doesn't serve you?

_____

_____

_____

_____

_____

_____

_____

How will you use fire to replace the negative with something beneficial?

_____

_____

_____

_____
_____
_____
_____
_____
_____

Write your visualization that you are using to help manifest your goal.

_____
_____
_____
_____
_____
_____
_____

## Day Nine

What abundant environment will you visit?

_____
_____

What is your daily mantra?

What is your daily affirmation?

How will you use water to release what doesn't serve you?

_____

_____

_____

_____

_____

_____

_____

_____

How will you use water to replace the negative with something beneficial?

_____

_____

_____

_____

_____

_____

_____

_____

How will you use air to release what doesn't serve you?

_____

_____

_____

_____

_____

_____

_____

_____

How will you use air to replace the negative with something beneficial?

_____

_____

_____

_____

_____

_____

_____

How will you use earth to release what doesn't serve you?

How will you use earth to replace the negative with something beneficial?

_____

_____

_____

How will you use fire to release what doesn't serve you?

_____

_____

_____

_____

_____

_____

_____

How will you use fire to replace the negative with something beneficial?

_____

_____

_____

_____

_____

_____

_____

_____

_____

Write your visualization that you are using to help manifest your goal.

_____

_____

_____

_____

_____

_____

_____

## Day Ten

What abundant environment will you visit?

_____

_____

_____

_____

_____

_____

_____

_____

_____

_____

What is your daily mantra?

_____

_____

_____

What is your daily affirmation?

_____

_____

_____

How will you use water to release what doesn't serve you?

_____

_____

How will you use water to replace the negative with something beneficial?

How will you use air to release what doesn't serve you?

How will you use air to replace the negative with something beneficial?

How will you use earth to release what doesn't serve you?

_____
_____
_____
_____
_____
_____
_____

How will you use earth to replace the negative with something beneficial?

_____
_____
_____
_____
_____
_____
_____
_____
_____
_____
_____

How will you use fire to release what doesn't serve you?

_____

_____

_____

_____

_____

_____

_____

How will you use fire to replace the negative with something beneficial?

_____

_____

_____

_____

_____

_____

_____

Write your visualization that you are using to help manifest your goal.

## Day Eleven

What abundant environment will you visit?

_____

_____

_____

_____

_____

What is your daily mantra?

_____

_____

_____

What is your daily affirmation?

_____

_____

_____

How will you use water to release what doesn't serve you?

_____

_____

_____

_____

How will you use water to replace the negative with something beneficial?

_____

How will you use air to release what doesn't serve you?

_____

_____

_____

_____

_____

_____

How will you use air to replace the negative with something beneficial?

_____

_____

_____

_____

_____

_____

_____

How will you use earth to release what doesn't serve you?

_____

_____

_____

_____

_____

_____

_____

_____

_____

How will you use earth to replace the negative with something beneficial?

_____

_____

_____

_____

_____

_____

_____

How will you use fire to release what doesn't serve you?

_____

_____

_____

_____

_____

_____

_____

_____

_____

How will you use fire to replace the negative with something beneficial?

_____

_____

_____

_____

_____

_____

_____

Write your visualization that you are using to help manifest your goal.

_____

_____

_____

_____

_____

_____

_____

_____

_____

# Day Twelve

What abundant environment will you visit?

_____

_____

_____

_____

_____

_____

_____

_____

_____
_____
_____

What is your daily mantra?

_____
_____
_____

What is your daily affirmation?

_____
_____
_____

How will you use water to release what doesn't serve you?

_____
_____
_____
_____
_____

_____

_____

_____

How will you use water to replace the negative with something beneficial?

_____

_____

_____

_____

_____

_____

How will you use air to release what doesn't serve you?

_____

_____

_____

_____

_____

How will you use air to replace the negative with something beneficial?

How will you use earth to release what doesn't serve you?

How will you use earth to replace the negative with something beneficial?

How will you use fire to release what doesn't serve you?

_____

_____

_____

_____

How will you use fire to replace the negative with something beneficial?

_____

_____

_____

_____

_____

_____

_____

_____

Write your visualization that you are using to help manifest your goal.

_____

_____

_____

_____

_____
_____
_____
_____

# Day Thirteen

What abundant environment will you visit?

_____
_____
_____
_____
_____
_____
_____
_____
_____
_____
_____

What is your daily mantra?

_____

_____

_____

_____

What is your daily affirmation?

_____

_____

_____

_____

How will you use water to release what doesn't serve you?

_____

_____

_____

_____

_____

_____

_____

How will you use water to replace the negative with something beneficial?

_____

_____

_____

_____

_____

_____

_____

How will you use air to release what doesn't serve you?

_____

_____

_____

_____

_____

_____

_____

_____

_____

How will you use air to replace the negative with something beneficial?

_____

_____

_____

_____

_____

_____

_____

How will you use earth to release what doesn't serve you?

_____

_____

_____

_____

_____

_____

_____

_____

How will you use earth to replace the negative with something beneficial?

_____

_____

_____

_____

_____

_____

_____

_____

How will you use fire to release what doesn't serve you?

_____

_____

_____

_____

_____

_____

_____

How will you use fire to replace the negative with something beneficial?

_____

_____

_____

_____

_____

_____

_____

_____

Write your visualization that you are using to help manifest your goal.

_____

_____

_____

_____

_____

_____

_____

# Day Fourteen

What abundant environment will you visit?

_____

_____

_____

_____

_____

_____

_____

_____

_____

What is your daily mantra?

_____

_____

_____

What is your daily affirmation?

_____

_____

_____

_____

How will you use water to release what doesn't serve you?

_____

_____

_____

_____

_____

_____

_____

How will you use water to replace the negative with something beneficial?

_____

_____

_____

_____

_____

_____

_____

_____

_____

How will you use air to release what doesn't serve you?

_____

_____

_____

_____

_____

_____

_____

How will you use air to replace the negative with something beneficial?

_____

_____

_____

_____

How will you use earth to release what doesn't serve you?

How will you use earth to replace the negative with something beneficial?

How will you use fire to release what doesn't serve you?

How will you use fire to replace the negative with something beneficial?

_____

_____

_____

_____

_____

Write your visualization that you are using to help manifest your goal.

_____

_____

_____

_____

_____

_____

## Day Fifteen

What abundant environment will you visit?

_____

_____

_____

_____

_____

_____

_____

_____

_____

_____

_____

What is your daily mantra?

_____

_____

_____

What is your daily affirmation?

_____

_____

_____

How will you use water to release what doesn't serve you?

_____

_____

_____

_____

_____

_____

_____

How will you use water to replace the negative with something beneficial?

_____

_____

_____

_____

_____

_____

_____

How will you use air to release what doesn't serve you?

_____

_____

_____

_____

_____

_____

_____

_____

How will you use air to replace the negative with something beneficial?

_____

_____

_____

_____

_____

_____

_____

How will you use earth to release what doesn't serve you?

How will you use earth to replace the negative with something beneficial?

_____

_____

_____

How will you use fire to release what doesn't serve you?

_____

_____

_____

_____

_____

_____

_____

How will you use fire to replace the negative with something beneficial?

_____

_____

_____

_____

_____

_____

_____

_____

_____

_____

Write your visualization that you are using to help manifest your goal.

_____

_____

_____

_____

_____

_____

# Day Sixteen

What abundant environment will you visit?

_____

_____

_____

_____

_____

_____

_____

_____

_____

_____

_____

What is your daily mantra?

_____

_____

_____

What is your daily affirmation?

_____

_____

_____

How will you use water to release what doesn't serve you?

_____

_____

_____
_____
_____
_____
_____
_____

How will you use water to replace the negative with something beneficial?

_____
_____
_____
_____
_____
_____

How will you use air to release what doesn't serve you?

_____
_____
_____

_____

_____

_____

_____

_____

_____

_____

_____

How will you use air to replace the negative with something beneficial?

_____

_____

_____

_____

_____

_____

_____

How will you use earth to release what doesn't serve you?

_____

_____

_____
_____
_____
_____
_____
_____
_____

How will you use earth to replace the negative with something beneficial?

_____
_____
_____
_____
_____
_____
_____
_____
_____

How will you use fire to release what doesn't serve you?

_____

_____

_____

_____

_____

_____

_____

How will you use fire to replace the negative with something beneficial?

_____

_____

_____

_____

_____

_____

_____

_____

Write your visualization that you are using to help manifest your goal.

_____

## Day Seventeen

What abundant environment will you visit?

_____

_____

_____

_____

_____

_____

_____

What is your daily mantra?

_____

_____

_____

What is your daily affirmation?

_____

_____

_____

How will you use water to release what doesn't serve you?

_____

_____

_____

How will you use water to replace the negative with something beneficial?

How will you use air to release what doesn't serve you?

_____
_____
_____
_____
_____
_____
_____

How will you use air to replace the negative with something beneficial?

_____
_____
_____
_____
_____
_____
_____
_____

How will you use earth to release what doesn't serve you?

_____
_____
_____

_____

_____

_____

_____

_____

_____

How will you use earth to replace the negative with something beneficial?

_____

_____

_____

_____

_____

_____

_____

_____

How will you use fire to release what doesn't serve you?

_____

_____

How will you use fire to replace the negative with something beneficial?

Write your visualization that you are using to help manifest your goal.

_____

_____

_____

_____

_____

_____

## Day Eighteen

What abundant environment will you visit?

_____

_____

_____

_____

_____

_____

_____

_____

_____

_____

_____

What is your daily mantra?

_____

_____

_____

What is your daily affirmation?

_____

_____

_____

How will you use water to release what doesn't serve you?

_____

_____

_____

_____

_____

_____

_____

_____

_____

How will you use water to replace the negative with something beneficial?

_____

_____

_____

_____

_____

_____

How will you use air to release what doesn't serve you?

_____

_____

_____

_____

_____

How will you use air to replace the negative with something beneficial?

How will you use earth to release what doesn't serve you?

_____

_____

_____

_____

_____

How will you use earth to replace the negative with something beneficial?

_____

_____

_____

_____

_____

_____

_____

_____

How will you use fire to release what doesn't serve you?

_____

_____

_____

_____

_____

_____

_____

_____

_____

How will you use fire to replace the negative with something beneficial?

_____

_____

_____

_____

_____

_____

_____

_____

_____

Write your visualization that you are using to help manifest your goal.

_____

_____

_____

_____

_____

_____

_____

_____

# Day Nineteen

What abundant environment will you visit?

_____

_____

_____

_____

_____

_____

_____

_____

_____

What is your daily mantra?

_____

_____

_____

_____

What is your daily affirmation?

_____

_____

_____

_____

How will you use water to release what doesn't serve you?

_____

_____

_____

_____

_____

_____

_____

_____

How will you use water to replace the negative with something beneficial?

_____

_____

_____

_____

_____

_____

How will you use air to release what doesn't serve you?

_____

_____

_____

_____

_____

_____

_____

_____

How will you use air to replace the negative with something beneficial?

_____

_____

_____

_____

_____

_____

_____

How will you use earth to release what doesn't serve you?

_____

_____

_____

_____

_____

_____

_____

How will you use earth to replace the negative with something beneficial?

_____

_____

_____

_____

_____

_____

_____

How will you use fire to release what doesn't serve you?

_____

_____

_____

_____

_____

_____

_____

How will you use fire to replace the negative with something beneficial?

_____

_____

_____

_____

_____

_____

_____

_____

Write your visualization that you are using to help manifest your goal.

_____

_____

_____

_____

_____

_____

_____

# Day Twenty

What abundant environment will you visit?

_____

_____

_____

_____

_____

_____

_____

_____

_____

_____

What is your daily mantra?

_____

_____

_____

_____

What is your daily affirmation?

_____

_____

_____

_____

How will you use water to release what doesn't serve you?

_____

_____

_____

_____

_____

_____

_____

How will you use water to replace the negative with something beneficial?

_____

_____

_____

_____

_____

_____

_____

_____

How will you use air to release what doesn't serve you?

_____

_____

_____

_____

_____

_____

_____

_____

How will you use air to replace the negative with something beneficial?

_____

_____

_____

_____

_____

How will you use earth to release what doesn't serve you?

How will you use earth to replace the negative with something beneficial?

_____

_____

_____

_____

_____

_____

How will you use fire to release what doesn't serve you?

_____

_____

_____

_____

_____

_____

_____

How will you use fire to replace the negative with something beneficial?

_____

_____

_____

_____

_____

_____

_____

_____

_____

_____

Write your visualization that you are using to help manifest your goal.

_____

_____

_____

_____

_____

_____

_____

# Day Twenty-One

What abundant environment will you visit?

_____

_____

What is your daily mantra?

What is your daily affirmation?

How will you use water to release what doesn't serve you?

_____

_____

_____

_____

_____

_____

_____

How will you use water to replace the negative with something beneficial?

_____

_____

_____

_____

_____

_____

_____

How will you use air to release what doesn't serve you?

_____

_____

_____

_____

_____

_____

_____

_____

How will you use air to replace the negative with something beneficial?

_____

_____

_____

_____

_____

_____

_____

How will you use earth to release what doesn't serve you?

How will you use earth to replace the negative with something beneficial?

_____

_____

_____

How will you use fire to release what doesn't serve you?

_____

_____

_____

_____

_____

_____

How will you use fire to replace the negative with something beneficial?

_____

_____

_____

_____

_____

_____

_____

_____

_____

Write your visualization that you are using to help manifest your goal.

_____

_____

_____

_____

_____

_____

_____

## Day Twenty-Two

What abundant environment will you visit?

_____

_____

_____

_____

_____

_____

_____

_____

_____

_____

_____

What is your daily mantra?

_____

_____

_____

What is your daily affirmation?

_____

_____

_____

_____

How will you use water to release what doesn't serve you?

_____

_____

_____

_____

_____

_____

_____

_____

How will you use water to replace the negative with something beneficial?

_____

_____

_____

_____

_____

_____

_____

_____

How will you use air to release what doesn't serve you?

_____

_____

_____

_____

_____

_____

_____

How will you use air to replace the negative with something beneficial?

_____

_____

_____

_____

_____

_____

How will you use earth to release what doesn't serve you?

How will you use earth to replace the negative with something beneficial?

How will you use fire to release what doesn't serve you?

How will you use fire to replace the negative with something beneficial?

Write your visualization that you are using to help manifest your goal.

# Day Twenty-Three

What abundant environment will you visit?

_____

_____

_____

_____

_____

_____

**What is your daily mantra?**

_____

_____

_____

**What is your daily affirmation?**

_____

_____

_____

**How will you use water to release what doesn't serve you?**

_____

_____

How will you use water to replace the negative with something beneficial?

How will you use air to release what doesn't serve you?

_____

_____

_____

_____

_____

_____

_____

How will you use air to replace the negative with something beneficial?

_____

_____

_____

_____

_____

_____

_____

How will you use earth to release what doesn't serve you?

_____

_____

_____

_____

_____

_____

_____

_____

_____


How will you use earth to replace the negative with something beneficial?

_____

_____

_____

_____

_____

_____

_____

_____

_____

_____

How will you use fire to release what doesn't serve you?

_____

_____

_____

_____

_____

_____

_____

_____

How will you use fire to replace the negative with something beneficial?

_____

_____

_____

_____

_____

_____

_____

_____

_____

Write your visualization that you are using to help manifest your goal.

_____

_____

_____

_____

_____

_____

## Day Twenty-Four

What abundant environment will you visit?

_____

_____

_____

_____

_____

_____
_____
_____
_____
_____
_____

What is your daily mantra?

_____
_____
_____

What is your daily affirmation?

_____
_____
_____

How will you use water to release what doesn't serve you?

_____
_____
_____

How will you use water to replace the negative with something beneficial?

How will you use air to release what doesn't serve you?

_____

_____

_____

_____

_____

How will you use air to replace the negative with something beneficial?

_____

_____

_____

_____

_____

_____

How will you use earth to release what doesn't serve you?

_____

_____

_____

How will you use earth to replace the negative with something beneficial?

How will you use fire to release what doesn't serve you?

_____

_____

_____

_____

_____

_____

How will you use fire to replace the negative with something beneficial?

_____

_____

_____

_____

_____

_____

_____

_____

Write your visualization that you are using to help manifest your goal.

_____

_____

_____
_____
_____
_____
_____
_____

# Day Twenty-Five

What abundant environment will you visit?

_____
_____
_____
_____
_____
_____
_____
_____
_____

_____

_____

What is your daily mantra?

_____

_____

_____

_____

What is your daily affirmation?

_____

_____

_____

_____

How will you use water to release what doesn't serve you?

_____

_____

_____

_____

_____

_____

_____

_____

How will you use water to replace the negative with something beneficial?

_____

_____

_____

_____

_____

_____

_____

How will you use air to release what doesn't serve you?

_____

_____

_____

_____

_____

_____

_____

_____

_____

How will you use air to replace the negative with something beneficial?

_____

_____

_____

_____

_____

_____

How will you use earth to release what doesn't serve you?

_____

_____

_____

_____

_____

_____

How will you use earth to replace the negative with something beneficial?

How will you use fire to release what doesn't serve you?

How will you use fire to replace the negative with something beneficial?

_____

_____

_____

_____

_____

_____

_____

Write your visualization that you are using to help manifest your goal.

_____

_____

_____

_____

_____

_____

_____

# Day Twenty-Six

What abundant environment will you visit?

_____

_____

_____

_____

_____

_____

_____

_____

_____

What is your daily mantra?

_____

_____

_____

_____

_____

What is your daily affirmation?

_____

_____

_____

How will you use water to release what doesn't serve you?

_____

_____

_____

_____

_____

_____

_____

How will you use water to replace the negative with something beneficial?

_____

_____

How will you use air to release what doesn't serve you?

How will you use air to replace the negative with something beneficial?

How will you use earth to release what doesn't serve you?

How will you use earth to replace the negative with something beneficial?

_____

_____

_____

_____

_____

_____

_____

_____

How will you use fire to release what doesn't serve you?

_____

_____

_____

_____

_____

_____

_____

_____

_____

_____

How will you use fire to replace the negative with something beneficial?

_____

_____

_____

_____

_____

_____

_____

Write your visualization that you are using to help manifest your goal.

_____

_____

_____

_____

_____

_____

_____

# Day Twenty-Seven

What abundant environment will you visit?

What is your daily mantra?

_____

_____

What is your daily affirmation?

_____

_____

_____

_____

How will you use water to release what doesn't serve you?

_____

_____

_____

_____

_____

_____

_____

_____

How will you use water to replace the negative with something beneficial?

_____

_____

_____

_____

_____

_____

_____

_____

How will you use air to release what doesn't serve you?

_____

_____

_____

_____

_____

_____

_____

_____

How will you use air to replace the negative with something beneficial?

_____

_____

_____

_____

_____

_____

_____

_____

_____

_____

How will you use earth to release what doesn't serve you?

_____

_____

_____

_____

_____

_____

_____

_____

How will you use earth to replace the negative with something beneficial?

_____

_____

_____

How will you use fire to release what doesn't serve you?

How will you use fire to replace the negative with something beneficial?

_____

_____

_____

_____

_____

_____

_____

_____

Write your visualization that you are using to help manifest your goal.

_____

_____

_____

_____

_____

_____

_____

_____

# Day Twenty-Eight

What abundant environment will you visit?

_____

_____

_____

_____

_____

_____

_____

_____

_____

_____

_____

What is your daily mantra?

_____

_____

_____

_____

What is your daily affirmation?

How will you use water to release what doesn't serve you?

How will you use water to replace the negative with something beneficial?

_____

_____

_____

_____

How will you use air to release what doesn't serve you?

_____

_____

_____

_____

_____

_____

_____

_____

How will you use air to replace the negative with something beneficial?

_____

_____

_____

_____

How will you use earth to release what doesn't serve you?

_____

How will you use earth to replace the negative with something beneficial?

_____

_____

_____

_____

_____

_____

_____

_____

How will you use fire to release what doesn't serve you?

_____

_____

_____

_____

_____

_____

_____

How will you use fire to replace the negative with something beneficial?

_____

_____

_____

_____

_____

_____

_____

_____

_____

Write your visualization that you are using to help manifest your goal.

_____

_____

_____

_____

_____

_____

_____

# Day Twenty-Nine

What abundant environment will you visit?

_____

_____

_____

_____

_____

_____

_____

_____

_____

What is your daily mantra?

_____

_____

_____

_____

What is your daily affirmation?

_____

_____

_____

_____

How will you use water to release what doesn't serve you?

_____

_____

_____

_____

_____

_____

_____

How will you use water to replace the negative with something beneficial?

_____

_____

_____

_____

How will you use air to release what doesn't serve you?

How will you use air to replace the negative with something beneficial?

_____

_____

_____

_____

_____

How will you use earth to release what doesn't serve you?

_____

_____

_____

_____

_____

_____

How will you use earth to replace the negative with something beneficial?

_____

_____

_____

_____

_____

_____

_____

_____

_____

How will you use fire to release what doesn't serve you?

_____

_____

_____

_____

_____

_____

_____

How will you use fire to replace the negative with something beneficial?

_____

_____

_____

Write your visualization that you are using to help manifest your goal.

# Day Thirty

What abundant environment will you visit?

_____

_____

_____

_____

_____

_____

_____

_____

_____

_____

_____

_____

What is your daily mantra?

_____

_____

_____

_____

What is your daily affirmation?

_____

_____

_____

_____

How will you use water to release what doesn't serve you?

_____

_____

_____

_____

_____

_____

_____

How will you use water to replace the negative with something beneficial?

_____

_____

_____

_____

_____

_____

_____

_____

_____

How will you use air to release what doesn't serve you?

_____

_____

_____

_____

_____

_____

_____

_____

How will you use air to replace the negative with something beneficial?

_____

_____

_____

_____

_____

_____

_____

_____

_____

How will you use earth to release what doesn't serve you?

_____

_____

_____

_____

_____

_____

How will you use earth to replace the negative with something beneficial?

_____

_____

_____

_____
_____
_____
_____
_____
_____

How will you use fire to release what doesn't serve you?

_____
_____
_____
_____
_____
_____
_____
_____

How will you use fire to replace the negative with something beneficial?

_____
_____
_____

_____

_____

_____

_____

_____

_____

_____

Write your visualization that you are using to help manifest your goal.

_____

_____

_____

_____

_____

_____

_____

_____

# Congratulations!

You are now empowered with the tools, knowledge, and resources to manifest your monetary goals and ambitions. While we may have reached the end of The Money Magick Workbook, this is just the beginning of your money magick journey. It is my desire that you continue to experience monetary increase and abundance in your life. Your willingness to show up for yourself and complete the exercises over the past 12 weeks have undoubtedly changed your relationship with money.

This workbook may have highlighted some strongly ingrained, uncomfortable, and detrimental beliefs that you hold about money. Continue to work on those beliefs and address them daily. This is an ongoing journey. Evolution at its finest. Why? Because you are the catalyst for your own change. It is powered by your desire to live in the abundance that is yours by divine right.

Money Magick has the ability to change your life in profound ways. When you are able to release the scarcity mindset, you are able to experience abundance not just in your bank account, but in all areas of your life.

It has been a pleasure to be your guide on this journey. I look forward to hearing your success stories. I am confident that once you create a money magick lifestyle you will experience a whole new level of prosperity, wealth, abundance, and opulence.

# About the Author

## Emme Rain

is an international best-selling author, keynote speaker, mentor, and business mogul. She has over 20 years of coaching and teaching experience in a variety of areas, including sexual and domestic violence, self-love, and healing, as well as personal and financial development. Her passion of personal development and teaching has led her to create Divinity Academy, a learning platform dedicated specifically to giving people the tools to become sovereign, abundant, and powerful.

Scan the QR code to connect with Emme Rain, shop from the Magickal Mystic website, or to learn more about the EmmePyre Emme Rain has created.

If you enjoyed this journal, please leave a review with the retailer you bought it from.